BELGICA

GAULISH VILLAGE

COMPENDIUM

LAUDANUM

AQUARIUM

TOTORUM

*LUTETIA

SPQR

ARMORICA

GAUL
(ROMAN CONQUEST)
50 BC

CELTICA

AQUITANIA

PROVINCIA

THE YEAR IS 50 BC. GAUL IS ENTIRELY OCCUPIED BY THE
ROMANS. WELL, NOT ENTIRELY ... ONE SMALL VILLAGE OF
INDOMITABLE GAULS STILL HOLDS OUT AGAINST THE INVADERS.
AND LIFE IS NOT EASY FOR THE ROMAN LEGIONARIES WHO
GARRISON THE FORTIFIED CAMPS OF TOTORUM, AQUARIUM,
LAUDANUM AND COMPENDIUM ...

ASTERIX, THE HERO OF THESE ADVENTURES. A SHREWD, CUNNING LITTLE WARRIOR, ALL PERILOUS MISSIONS ARE IMMEDIATELY ENTRUSTED TO HIM. ASTERIX GETS HIS SUPERHUMAN STRENGTH FROM THE MAGIC POTION BREWED BY THE DRUID GETAFIX . . .

OBELIX, ASTERIX'S INSEPARABLE FRIEND. A MENHIR DELIVERY MAN BY TRADE, ADDICTED TO WILD BOAR. OBELIX IS ALWAYS READY TO DROP EVERYTHING AND GO OFF ON A NEW ADVENTURE WITH ASTERIX – SO LONG AS THERE'S WILD BOAR TO EAT, AND PLENTY OF FIGHTING. HIS CONSTANT COMPANION IS DOGMATIX, THE ONLY KNOWN CANINE ECOLOGIST, WHO HOWLS WITH DESPAIR WHEN A TREE IS CUT DOWN.

GETAFIX, THE VENERABLE VILLAGE DRUID, GATHERS MISTLETOE AND BREWS MAGIC POTIONS. HIS SPECIALITY IS THE POTION WHICH GIVES THE DRINKER SUPERHUMAN STRENGTH. BUT GETAFIX ALSO HAS OTHER RECIPES UP HIS SLEEVE . . .

CACOFONIX, THE BARD. OPINION IS DIVIDED AS TO HIS MUSICAL GIFTS. CACOFONIX THINKS HE'S A GENIUS. EVERY-ONE ELSE THINKS HE'S UNSPEAKABLE. BUT SO LONG AS HE DOESN'T SPEAK, LET ALONE SING, EVERYBODY LIKES HIM . . .

FINALLY, VITALSTATISTIX, THE CHIEF OF THE TRIBE. MAJESTIC, BRAVE AND HOT-TEMPERED, THE OLD WARRIOR IS RESPECTED BY HIS MEN AND FEARED BY HIS ENEMIES. VITALSTATISTIX HIMSELF HAS ONLY ONE FEAR, HE IS AFRAID THE SKY MAY FALL ON HIS HEAD TOMORROW. BUT AS HE ALWAYS SAYS, TOMORROW NEVER COMES.

THE ONLY THING THAT THE GAULS ARE AFRAID OF IS THE SKY FALLING ON THEIR HEADS, AN EVENT WHICH SEEMS IMMINENT AS A TERRIBLE STORM BATTERS THE LITTLE VILLAGE WE KNOW SO WELL.

BRRRAOMM!

ALL THE TOP PEOPLE IN THE VILLAGE HAVE GATHERED TOGETHER IN THE HOUSE OF CHIEF VITALSTATISTIX...

IF ONLY GETAFIX WASN'T AWAY AT THE DRUIDS' ANNUAL CONFERENCE IN THE FOREST OF THE CARNUTES HE'D LOOK AFTER US...

THERE'S NOTHING TO BE AFRAID OF! WE'VE HAD STORMS BEFORE. THIS IS QUITE A BAD ONE, I AGREE, BUT...

SUPPOSE I SING SOMETHING TO BOOST OUR MORALE?

BRRRAOM!

TARANIS, THE GOD OF THUNDER, DOESN'T THINK MUCH OF THAT SUGGESTION!

THAT'S ONE GOD WITH HIS HEAD SCREWED ON RIGHT!

5

7

SCRUNCH! SCRUNCH!

WHAT IS YOUR NAME, TRAVELLER?

MY NAME IS PROLIX. I WANDER AROUND THE COUNTRY STOPPING WHERE I KNOW I SHALL BE WELL RECEIVED. I KNEW THAT THE STORM WAS GOING TO BREAK, SO I HURRIED TO YOUR HOME, WHERE I KNEW I COULD COUNT ON YOUR HOSPITALITY...

...EVEN IF CERTAIN PEOPLE DO HAVE A STRANGE WAY OF SHARING MILK AND BOAR... BUT I KNEW THAT TOO.

H-HOW DID YOU KNOW ALL THAT?

I AM A SOOTHSAYER!

A SOOTHSAYER!?

HO, HO!

BRRRAOM!

SOMEONE IN THIS ROOM IS SCEPTICAL, AND TARANIS DOESN'T LIKE THAT!

OF COURSE NOT! IT MUST BE THIS IDIOT WHO WAS GOING TO SING! ALL HE DOES IS ANNOY TARANIS!

REALLY... I ASSURE YOU!

PLEASE FORGIVE MY MEN, SOOTHSAYER. THEY SPEND ALL THEIR TIME QUARRELLING.

I KNOW.

...STERIX'S SCEPTICISM ...S NO EFFECT. ...UBJECTED TO THE ...FLUENCE OF SO ...ANY GODS, WHO BOTH ...ROTECT AND THREATEN ...EM, THE NATIONS ...F ANTIQUITY WOULD ...KE TO HAVE ADVANCE ...OTICE OF THEIR WHIMS. ...ERE WE MUST INSERT ...PARENTHESIS...

A PARENTHESIS WHICH IS NECESSARY FOR A BRIEF EXPLANATION OF SOOTHSAYERS, ORACLES, PROPHETS, AUGURERS, HARUSPICES AND OTHER INTERPRETERS OF THE SIBYLLINE BOOKS...

O SOOTHSAYER, WILL THE GODS LOOK KINDLY ON THE HARVEST?

SOOTHSAYERS READ THE FUTURE IN THE WAY BIRDS FLY...

YES, FARMER, THE GODS WILL SEND RAIN FOR YOUR FIELDS!

...IN THE APPETITE OF THE SACRED ...EESE...

THE GOOSE LIVER PÂTÉ WILL BE GOOD THIS YEAR! THE GODS HAVE SPOKEN!

...AND ABOVE ALL IN THE ENTRAILS OF SACRIFICIAL ANIMALS.

YOU CAN SET SAIL. THE GODS WILL BE KIND. THERE'S NOT THE LEAST LITTLE STORM IN THE OFFING.

THE PREDICTIONS OF THE ENTRAILS ARE NOT ALWAYS CORRECT...

I THOUGHT IT WAS JUST A LOAD OF TRIPE!

EVEN THE GREATEST CONSULT THE AUGURIES...

...AND AS LONG AS BRUTUS IS NEAR YOU, O CAESAR, YOU WILL HAVE NOTHING TO FEAR!

IF CERTAIN VISIONARIES HAVE A REASONABLE IDEA OF WHAT THE FUTURE HOLDS...

...GENERALLY THEY SAY ANY OLD THING!

IN SHORT, THEY ARE CHARLATANS WHO THRIVE ON CREDULITY, FEAR AND HUMAN SUPERSTITION. HERE WE CLOSE THE PARENTHESIS.

11

SOOTHSAYER, DON'T LEAVE! I WANT TO CONSULT YOU ABOUT MY FUTURE.

NO, NO, NO. THERE ARE SCEPTICS IN YOUR VILLAGE!

THAT LITTLE MAN WITH THE YELLOW MOUSTACHE, AND THE FAT MONSTER WHO WON'T LET ANYONE READ HIS DOG!...

THEY'RE JUST BARBARIANS... YOU MUSTN'T TAKE ANY NOTICE OF THEM. PLEASE STAY!

I FORESEE DIFFICULTIES WITH YOUR BARBARIANS IF I GO BACK TO THE VILLAGE. CAN'T YOU GET THOSE TWO THROWN OUT?

THROW OUT ASTERIX AND OBELIX? WE COULDN'T DO THAT!

OF COURSE, I COULD ALWAYS CAMP IN THIS CLEARING FOR THE TIME BEING...

OH, YES! AND I'LL MAKE SURE ASTERIX AND OBELIX DON'T COME INTO THE FOREST ANY MORE.

I'LL BRING EVERYTHING YOU NEED... THINGS TO EAT...

OH, NO! WE SOOTHSAYERS LEAD A LIFE OF MEDITATION...

10

JUST BRING ME SOMETHING TO READ: BOARS, DUCKS, CHICKENS, CAKES, BEER...

CAN YOU READ BEER TOO?

IF IT'S WELL KEPT, IT BECOMES VERY LEGIBLE.

YOU CAN HAVE ALL THAT, BUT JUST TELL ME WHAT THE GODS HAVE IN STORE FOR ME...

HMMM...

THE FLIGHT OF THOSE SWALLOWS TELLS ME THAT YOU WILL NOT SPEND ALL YOUR LIFE IN THIS WRETCHED VILLAGE.

BUT MY HUSBAND IS THE CHIEF!

HE WILL BE CALLED TO HIGHER THINGS... I SHALL NEED CUSHIONS AS WELL...

WILL MY RICH BROTHER HOMEOPATHIX TAKE HIM ON AS A BUSINESS PARTNER IN LUTETIA?

I WAS JUST GOING TO SAY SO! NOW LEAVE ME. I MUST MEDITATE!

10

14

15

THE NEXT DAY...

APPARENTLY YOU READ MY FISH AND TOLD MY WIFE IT WOULD HAVE A WIDE CIRCULATION. SHALL I HAVE A CHAIN OF FISHMONGERS' SHOPS?

THAT'S RIGHT. FOR MORE DETAILS, I SHALL HAVE TO READ GOLD.

WOULD SESTERTII DO?

YES, BUT DON'T FORGET THE OFFICIAL RATE OF EXCHANGE: ONE HUNDRED SESTERTII TO THE AURUS.*

* GOLD COIN

HALLO! TAKING YOUR CHICKENS FOR A WALK?

YES...

CLUCK?

WELL, YOUR WIFE TAKES HER FISHES FOR A WALK.

IDIOT!

CLUCK!

ER... I'M JUST GOING FOR A DRINK IN THE FOREST...

THERE ARE SOME FUNNY GOINGS-ON HERE...

WHAT'S GOING ON IS THEY'RE ALL MAKING FOR THE FOREST, AND THEY'RE HAPPY, AND HERE'S ME BORED TO TEARS WITH NOTHING TO DO!

IT'S THE CLOSE SEASON FOR MENHIRS, AND DOGMATIX IS PINING FOR SOME TREES!...

WHERE ARE YOU GOING?

SOME PEOPLE TAKE THEIR FISHES OR THEIR CHICKENS FOR A WALK, I TAKE MY DOG! SO SUCKS TO PIGGYWIGGY!

14

WHERE IS HE?

WHERE IS WHO?

YOU'VE FRIGHTENED HIM AWAY! WHEN YOUR CHIEF TOLD YOU NOT TO COME INTO THE FOREST!

THIS WILL BRING US GREAT MISFORTUNE! THE SOOTHSAYER FORETOLD IT!

THE SOOTHSAYER? IMPEDIMENTA, WAIT FOR ME!...

ASTERIX HAS DRIVEN THE SOOTHSAYER AWAY!

HE MUST BE MAD! THE SOOTHSAYER FORETOLD GREAT MISFORTUNES IF HE WAS DRIVEN AWAY!

YOU HAVE DONE A VERY FOOLISH THING, ASTERIX. THE SOOTHSAYER WARNED ME TOO...

OH, SO YOU WENT TO SEE HIM AS WELL...

WELL... ER... ONLY ONCE! FORESIGHT IS ONE OF THE ATTRIBUTES OF A CHIEFTAIN, AND...

HE TOLD ME THE MAN I LOVE WOULD BECOME STRONG AND HANDSOME!

WELL, HE WAS RIGHT THERE, ANYWAY!

NOW LISTEN: IF I'D KNOWN THE SOOTHSAYER WAS IN THE FOREST, I PROBABLY WOULD HAVE DRIVEN HIM OFF! BUT I DIDN'T KNOW AND I HAVEN'T THE FAINTEST IDEA WHAT'S GOING ON!

FISHMONGER UNHYGIENIX

THE EXPLANATION IS TO BE FOUND AT THIS VERY MOMENT, IN THE FORTIFIED ROMAN CAMP OF COMPENDIUM...

AVE, CENTURION VOLUPTUOUS ARTERIOSCLEROSUS!

AVE. LET'S HAVE YOUR REPORT.

BONK!

ON PROCEEDING ON PATROL, FOR WHICH YOU GAVE THE ORDERS TO PROCEED WITH, WE FOUND THIS 'ERE INDIVIDUAL IN A CLEARING, AND AFTER A CAUTION HE MADE A STATEMENT WHAT WE WERE NOT VERY SATISFIED WITH.

ARE YOU ONE OF THOSE CRAZY GAULS WHO STILL HOLD OUT AGAINST THE INVADERS?

ME? OH, NO, NO! I DON'T HOLD OUT AGAINST ANYONE!

I'M JUST A SOOTHSAYER.

A SOOTHSAYER? ARE YOU A REAL GAULISH SOOTHSAYER?

OF COURSE... WAIT... I FORESEE THAT YOU WILL BE PROMOTED.

18A

YOU'RE OUT OF LUCK, SOOTHSAYER. WE'VE GOT ORDERS FROM ROME TO ARREST ALL GAULISH SOOTHSAYERS. OUR AUGURERS HAVE WARNED CAESAR THAT GAULISH SOOTHSAYERS ARE A THREAT TO SECURITY...

SO YOU'LL BE SHIPPED OFF TO A MINE IN...

NO, NO, NO! I WAS ONLY JOKING. I'M NOT A REAL SOOTHSAYER, I'M A FAKE.

I TAKE ADVANTAGE OF PEOPLE'S CREDULITY TO LIVE WITHOUT WORKING...

BUT YOU JUST FORETOLD THAT I WOULD BE PROMOTED, ALL THE SAME...

NO, NO, OF COURSE NOT. DON'T BE ABSURD!

JUST WHAT I WAS SAYING...

WHEN I WANT YOUR OPINION I'LL ASK FOR IT, IDIOT! THIS INDIVIDUAL HAS NOT CONVINCED ME! HE IS A SUSPECT!

YES SIR!

18B

BONG.

BONK.

YOU DID A VERY SILLY THING THERE, ASTERIX! IT IS DANGEROUS TO CROSS A SOOTHSAYER!

THAT IMPOSTOR TOOK YOUR GOLD, LIVED OFF YOUR FOOD AND DRINK, AND NOW HE'S SIMPLY GONE OFF TO LOOK FOR SOME MORE STUPID PEOPLE!

WELL, I DON'T THINK HE WAS AN IMPOSTOR. I DON'T LIKE HIS CHOICE OF READING MATTER, BUT SOME OF WHAT HE SAID WAS RIGHT.

OH NO, OBELIX! NOT YOU TOO!

FOR ONCE YOUR FAT FRIEND HAS SAID SOMETHING SENSIBLE...

I AM NOT FAT! I'M A GREAT WARRIOR WITH RED PIGTAILS.

THE SOOTHSAYER! THE SOOTHSAYER IS BACK!

LOOK!

YES, I AM BACK TO TELL YOU THAT MISFORTUNE IS UPON YOU, GAULS! YOUR VILLAGE IS CURSED BY THE GODS!

THE VERY AIR YOU BREATHE WILL COME FROM THE DEPTHS OF HELL. IT WILL BE FOUL, POISONED, AND YOUR FACES WILL TURN A GHASTLY HUE...

FLEE! FLEE, RASH PEOPLE! IT IS YOUR ONLY CHANCE OF SURVIVAL! DON'T SAY I DIDN'T WARN YOU!

LAUNCH THE BOATS!

COME ON, BOYS! WE'RE GOING ON BOARD!

ARE YOU ALL RIGHT, GERIATRIX, MY LOVE?

GLUG, GLUG, GLUG!

DO YOU REALLY THINK THE SOOTHSAYER IS HAVING US ON?

I'M SURE OF IT! I DON'T KNOW WHAT HE TOLD YOU, BUT THE BEST THING TO DO WOULD BE TO LAUGH IT OFF.

I DON'T FEEL MUCH LIKE LAUGHING.

LET'S GO AND HIDE IN THE FOREST AND SEE WHAT HAPPENS NEXT.

MEANWHILE...

THERE YOU ARE! THEY'VE LEFT, JUST LIKE I TOLD YOU THEY WOULD.

I NEVER DOUBTED IT. YOU SOOTHSAYERS HAVE GREAT POWERS.

RIGHT. DO WE LOCK HIM UP?

YOU PROMISED ME MY LIBERTY! I'M NOT A SOOTHSAYER! I'M A CON MAN, THAT'S ALL!

22

T'S GO OFF TO THE VILLAGE AND CHECK UP ON THESE STATEMENTS OF YOURS.

...SO THEN I GOT THE IDEA OF GOING ON ABOUT THE FOUL AIR, BECAUSE, YOU SEE, I LIVE NEAR A TANNERY IN LUTETIA, SO...

OH, SO IT WASN'T A GENUINE PREDICTION?

CAN'T MAKE ANY GENUINE PREDICTIONS! IF I COULD HAVE FORESEEN HOW THIS WAS GOING TO TURN OUT I'D HAVE STAYED AT HOME NEXT DOOR TO THAT TANNERY!

SSH... WE'RE NEAR THE VILLAGE... ALL SEEMS QUIET, BUT YOU NEVER KNOW WITH THOSE GAULS!

WE NEED A SCOUT TO GO ON AHEAD. I WANT A VOLUNTEER.

SIR!

AND YOU CAN TAKE THE SOOTHSAYER WITH YOU.

I KNEW IT.

I KNOW.

NO YOU DON'T! NO YOU DON'T!

DO WE LOCK HIM UP, THEN?

23

LOOK, ASTERIX! TWO OF THEM HAVE GONE IN. WE'RE NOT GOING TO LET ANY ROMANS TAKE OVER OUR VILLAGE, ARE WE?

THEY'RE ONLY PASSING THROUGH. THAT'S A PROMISE, OBELIX!

ALL CLEAR.

ER... CENTURION... DO YOU THINK THIS IS REALLY WISE? IT COULD BE AN AMBUSH... YOU KNOW WHAT THESE GAULS ARE LIKE...

NO, NO, MY GOOD FELLOW! SOOTHSAYERS ARE NEVER WRONG, YOU KNOW! RIGHT, FORWARD MARCH, IV ABREAST!

THE LIBERATION OF A CITY IS ALWAYS A MOVING EXPERIENCE!

EMPTY, DESERTED AND UNINHABITED, AS YOU MIGHT SAY, O CENTURION!

FISHMONGER
UNHYG

YOU ARE TO START FOR ROME, BEARING A MESSAGE FOR CAESAR. YOU WILL TELL HIM: "ALL GAUL IS OCCUPIED." HE WILL ASK "ALL?" YOU WILL REPLY: "ALL!" HE WILL UNDERSTAND.

YOU'LL BE SURE TO GET PROMOTION, SIR, SAME AS THIS 'ERE SOOTHSAYER WAS SOOTHSAYING!

OF COURSE.

NO! I NEVER! I NEVER SAID ANY SUCH THING!

OH? AND WHY NOT? HAVE THE GODS SHOWN YOU SOMETHING NASTY IN MY FUTURE THEN?

I TELL YOU, I DON'T KNOW A THING ABOUT IT!

ANSWER ME, OR I'LL HAVE YOU OPENED UP SO YOU CAN READ YOUR OWN ENTRAILS!

NO! NO! YOU'LL GET PROMOTION ALL RIGHT!

DO WE LOCK HIM UP, THEN?

OUR DRUID, GETAFIX!

TARANIS, THE GOD OF STORMS AND THUNDER, IS IN MELLOW MOOD, AND SENDS A GENTLE BREEZE, WAFTING THROUGH THE AIR A SMELL WHICH WAS STILL UNFAMILIAR IN THE YEAR 50 BC...

YUK!

I SAY, DO YOU SMELL A FUNNY KIND OF SMELL, ALL OF A SUDDEN?

SNIFF! SNIFF!

A FUNNY KIND OF SMELL?

YES, A FUNNY KIND OF SMELL.

IT'S A BIT LIKE WHERE I LIVE IN ROME.

SNIFF! SNIFF!

YOU LIVE NEAR A TANNERY, I SUPPOSE?

YES! HE GOT IT RIGHT! HE IS A SOOTHSAYER!

OOOOOH... CENTURION!

THE AIR IN THIS VILLAGE ISN'T FIT TO BREATHE... IT'S PESTILENTIAL, THAT'S WHAT IT IS!

PES... PESTILENTIAL?

YOU TAKE MY WORD FOR IT. I'M A VETERAN, I AM. I'VE KNOWN PLENTY OF CAMPS AND BARRACKS, BUT I NEVER SMELT ANYTHING LIKE THIS BEFORE!

SNIFF! SNIFF!

I FORGOT MY LYRE, SO I WENT BACK TO THE VILLAGE TO GET IT, AND I FOUND MYSELF BREATHING FOUL AIR... AIR FROM THE DEPTHS OF HELL! EVEN THE ROMANS HAD TO RUN FOR IT!

YOU SEE? YOU SEE? WE SHOULD HAVE GONE TO LUTETIA, LIKE THE SOOTHSAYER SAID! YOU STUPID GREAT BOAR!

DARLING... AREN'T I YOUR PIGGYWIGGY ANY MORE?

WELL, I'LL JUST HAVE TO DO WITHOUT MY LYRE.

O, I DO LIKE TO BE BESIDE THE LITUS...

TCHOUF!

ARE YOU CRAZY? COME BACK!

I'D RATHER BREATHE FOUL AIR THAN LISTEN TO THAT!

WHAT ARE YOU SINGING FOR, ANYWAY?

THE SOOTHSAYER TOLD ME VOICES LIKE MINE WERE GOING TO BE VERY POPULAR IN THE FUTURE. I'M PRACTISING.

WELL, ALL WE HAVE TO DO NOW IS WAIT FOR FRESH AIR TO DISPERSE THE BAD SMELL IN THE VILLAGE, AND THEN WE'LL GO AND LOOK FOR OUR FRIENDS...

AND AS FOR THE ROMANS, I'M COUNTING ON YOU. YOU'RE SURE TO THINK OF SOMETHING.

I'VE THOUGHT OF SOMETHING ALREADY. WE GO TO THEIR CAMP AND BASH THE WHOLE PLACE UP!

WHEREVER DO YOU GET ALL THESE ORIGINAL IDEAS?

A HANDSOME WARRIOR WITH RED PIGTAILS, YES! BUT I'M NOT JUST A PRETTY FACE!

MEANWHILE...

PHEW! THAT'S BETTER... IN FACT, I'D SAY ALL WAS GOING WELL!

NOTWITHSTANDING WHICH, WE'VE HAD TO CLEAR OUT OF THE VILLAGE WHAT WE OCCUPIED.

HUH! THANKS TO THE SOOTHSAYER, WE HAVE PUT THE REBEL GAULS TO FLIGHT, AND THAT'S THE MAIN THING.

RIGHT, DO WE LOCK HIM UP THIS TIME, THEN?

NO!

BUT ORDERS IS...

THIS MAN IS A FRAUD! THERE IS NO REASON FOR US TO IMPRISON HIM.

EXCUSING THE LIBERTY, SIR, BUT I DON'T QUITE GET YOUR MEANING...

OF COURSE YOU DON'T. THAT'S THE KIND OF THING THAT MAKES ME A CENTURIO WHILE YOU'RE JUST AN OPTIONE. *

BONG! BONG! BONG!

* ADJUTANT

HE'S RIGHT THERE...

COME TO MY TENT. I WANT A WORD WITH YOU.

WELL, YOU'VE PROVED IT NOW: YOU REALLY ARE A SOOTHSAYER. THE GODS ARE ANGRY WITH THOSE WHO DOUBTED YOU, AND THEY HAVE CURSED THE GAULISH VILLAGE...

WELL... I MUST CONFESS I...

I OUGHT TO HAVE YOU ARRESTED, BUT YOU MIGHT COME IN USEFUL TO ME IN MY FUTURE CAREER... WITH THE HELP OF YOUR PREDICTIONS AND ADVICE I COULD GO FAR! I MIGHT EVEN RISE TO THE POSITION OF...

CAESAR!

AND YOU WILL NOT FIND ME UNGRATEFUL. BUT REMEMBER, IF YOU ARE NOT A REAL SOOTHSAYER, IF YOU'VE BEEN HAVING ME ON, I WILL NEVER FORGIVE YOU!!!

GETAFIX! YOU'RE BACK AT LAST!

MAYBE YOU CAN APPEASE THE ANGER OF THE GODS, WHICH HAS FALLEN UPON OUR POOR VILLAGE...

NONSENSE! YOU'RE VICTIMS OF YOUR OWN CREDULITY, THAT'S ALL!

OH, WAIT A MINUTE, GETAFIX! I'VE SEEN THE VILLAGE! I'VE BREATHED THE FOUL AIR, STRAIGHT FROM THE DEPTHS OF HELL! I'VE SEEN THE ROMANS GO GREEN!

THAT'S RIGHT! OUR BARD MAY HAVE A VOICE LIKE A SISTRUM,* BUT HE DOESN'T TELL LIES.

* A KIND OF METAL RATTLE

YOU KNOW WHAT YOUR BARD HAS TO SAY TO YOU IN HIS VOICE LIKE A SISTRUM?

CALM DOWN, CALM DOWN! I'LL GIVE YOU A LITTLE DEMONSTRATION OF THE ANGER OF THE GODS.

OBELIX! EMPTY THAT CAULDRON AND...

...BRING IT OVER HERE.

THERE YOU ARE!

SOON AFTERWARDS...

VERY GOOD! NOW, ALL OF YOU GO OVER THERE, THE WAY THE WIND'S BLOWING.

HOLD IT!

PSSCHCHCHCH!

BY TOUTATIS! I CAN'T STAND THIS!

?

STOP IT, BY BELENOS! STOP IT!

OOOOH!

WHAT ON EARTH IS THE MATTER WITH YOU?

CHIEF, DO YOU THINK YOU COULD LOWER YOURSELF TO THE LEVEL OF OUR PROBLEMS FOR A MOMENT?

THERE YOU ARE, THAT'S THE ANGER OF THE GODS: A CONCOCTION IN A CAULDRON!

THE SMELL DOESN'T SEEM TO BOTHER YOU ALL THAT MUCH...

HUH, WELL, WHAT WITH HIS FISH...

SPLATCH!

37

I EXPECT YOU KNOW WHAT TO DO NOW?

I THINK SO, GETAFIX...

WE GO BACK TO THE VILLAGE TONIGHT. **IN PEACE AND QUIET!**

AND THAT VERY NIGHT...

DROP ANCHOR!

DON'T YOU THINK IT'S A BIT DANGEROUS TO ANCHOR IN BETWEEN THE GAULISH COAST AND THIS UNKNOWN ISLAND, CAP'N?

SHIVER ME TIMBERS, NO! WE CONSULTED THE ENTRAILS OF A MACKEREL, AND THE ORACLE WAS ABSOLUTELY POSITIVE: IT'S SAFE AS HOUSES TO ANCHOR HERE OVERNIGHT.

NEXT MORNING...

THIS IS TERRIBLE! A SHOAL OF GAULS HAS CROSSED OUR PATH!

GLUG! GLUG! GLUG! GLUG! GLUG!

I'VE HAD A BELLYFUL OF ENTRAILS!

STOP BELLYACHING! I THOUGHT YOU HAD MORE GUTS!

I MUST SAY, IT'S NICE TO BE HOME!

WELL, I MUST SAY I THINK WE'D HAVE BEEN BETTER OFF IN LUTETIA, LIKE THE SOOTHSAYER SAID.

BUT HE WASN'T REALLY A SOOTHSAYER!

WHAT MAKES YOU SO SURE?

I'VE BEEN TALKING TO GERIATRIX'S WIFE AND TO BACTERIA, AND THEY'RE NOT CONVINCED. THAT'S WHY I THOUGHT LUTETIA MIGHT BE THE PLACE...

GETAFIX, THE WOMEN AREN'T CONVINCED THAT HE'S A FRAUD...

OF COURSE THEY'RE NOT. HE ONLY FORETOLD PLEASANT THINGS FOR THEM, SUCH AS THEIR HUSBANDS BECOMING HANDSOME AND INTELLIGENT...

SUPPOSE WE GAVE THAT SOOTHSAYER A SURPRISE?

ASTERIX, I'M PROUD OF YOU! IF WE GIVE THE SOOTHSAYER A SURPRISE THAT WILL PROVE THAT HE'S NOT REALLY A SOOTHSAYER!

OH, SO YOU THINK I NEED TO BECOME HANDSOME AND INTELLIGENT, DO YOU?

YOU ARRANGE A LITTLE SURPRISE, ASTERIX! I'M OFF TO MAKE SOME MAGIC POTION!

SOON AFTERWARDS...

WELL, ARE WE ALL AGREED? IF THE SOOTHSAYER DOESN'T GUESS WHAT'S IN STORE FOR HIM, WILL YOU BELIEVE THAT HE ISN'T A REAL SOOTHSAYER?

YOU, GAUL! THE CENTURION WANTS YOU IN HIS TENT.

NOT AGAIN!

AH, SOOTHSAYER! TELL ME ABOUT MY FUTURE!

FLOP!

BUT I'VE TOLD IT ALL ALREADY: THE GODS WILL PROTECT YOU, YOU'LL GET PROMOTION, YOU'LL...

I KNOW, I KNOW, BUT TELL ME WHAT IT WILL BE LIKE WHEN I'M CAESAR.

WELL, YOU'LL BE VERY POWERFUL, AND THE COMMON PEOPLE WILL FEAR YOU...

EXCELLENT, EXCELLENT... AND HOW ABOUT CLEOPATRA?

CLEOPATRA? WHAT DO YOU MEAN, CLEOPATRA?

HAVEN'T YOU HEARD OF CLEOPATRA?

YES, YES, YES!

CLEOPATRA WILL FORGET JULIUS CAESAR IN NO TIME, AND SHE'LL FALL MADLY IN LOVE WITH YOU...

GREAT! AND WILL SHE INVITE ME ON BOARD HER BARGE? AND WILL THERE BE DANCING GIRLS? AND WILL THEY GIVE ME EXQUISITE DISHES TO EAT?

YES, YES, THEY'LL GIVE YOU... THEY'LL GIVE YOU PRESERVED PIGS' EARS.

PRESERVED PIGS' EARS? SOOTHSAYER, YOU'RE A MARVEL!

AND WHILE THE UNSUSPECTING ROMANS ARE LIVING IN A FOOL'S PARADISE, NEAR THE CAMP...

WAIT HERE, AND DON'T MAKE ANY NOISE. OBELIX AND I WILL SEE TO THE SENTRIES.

SSSH!

?

THE GAULS!!!

GAULS INSIDE THE CAMP, AND YOU DIDN'T WARN ME?!!

BUT HOW WAS I TO KNOW?

LEAVE HIM TO ME!

?

HOW WERE YOU TO KNOW? YOU MEAN TO SAY YOU MADE UP ALL THAT ABOUT LUTETIA? AND PIGGYWIGGY GOING INTO PARTNERSHIP WITH MY BROTHER?

GOOD SHOT, MADAM!

PAFF!

PAFF!

CHARGE!

THAT WAS MY LITTLE 'PEDIMENTA, THAT WAS!

ZZWWIP!

NO WOMEN ALLOWED IN CAMP! NO WOMEN ALLOWED IN CAMP!

BUT, MY DEAR MADAM, WHAT DO YOU WANT WITH ME?

THE GODS KNOW WHAT TOMORROW MAY BRING, BUT I'M THROUGH WITH SOOTHSAYING!

AND IF EVER I CHANGE MY MIND, MAY TARANIS MAKE THE SKY FALL ON MY HEAD!

BRAOUM!

HOWEVER, THE ANGER OF TARANIS IS SHORT-LIVED...

...AND SOON TOUTATIS IS MAKING THE SUN SHINE DOWN ON THE VILLAGE, AT PEACE ONCE AGAIN.

WELL, OBELIX, OLD FRIEND, I DON'T KNOW WHAT THE SOOTHSAYER SAID TO YOU, BUT I'M SURE YOU'LL BE HAPPY!

YOU'RE NOT A SOOTHSAYER, ASTERIX.

OH, AREN'T I? DIDN'T I TELL YOU THERE'D BE ANOTHER BANQUET IN THIS VILLAGE... WELL, SO THERE WILL BE, THIS VERY EVENING!

HOW RIGHT YOU ARE! YOU DID FORETELL IT!

BUT THAT EVENING ALL IS FORGIVEN AND FORGOTTEN. UNDER THE STARS AND THE PROTECTION OF TOUTATIS, GOD OF THE TRIBE, ROSMERTA, THE GODDESS OF PLENTY, AND CERNUNNOS, THE GOD OF NATURE, THE GAULS, UNITED ONCE AGAIN, ENJOY THE PRESENT AND TAKE NO THOUGHT FOR THE FUTURE.

THE END

UDERZO & GOSCINNY 8.72